Baby-sitting Barney

Written by Jeanne Willis
Illustrated by Jess Mikhail

Sid went to Nan's for tea.
Nan was baby-sitting.
The baby was called Barney.

Barney did not sleep.
He screamed and screamed.
Sid looked grumpy.

"Maybe he's hungry. Let's feed him," said Nan. "Have some yummy mashed swedes and milk."

Barney ate the swedes and milk.
But then he started screaming.

"He's got a windy tummy," said Nan.
Barney was sick on Sid's jeans.

"He's got a soggy nappy," said Nan.

Sid put Barney in his buggy.
But Barney screamed and screamed.

Barney grabbed Sid's hair.

"Cheeky!" said Nan.

"Ow!" shrieked Sid. "He's a meany."

"You need to carry him," said Nan.
Sid carried Barney up and down.
Barney looked sleepy.

Sid put Barney back in the buggy.
But Barney screamed and screamed.
"What's up Barney?" asked Sid.

"He's just not sleepy," said Nan. "Read him a story."

Barney liked Sid's story.

But it did not make Barney sleepy.

He yelled for Sid to keep reading!

At six o'clock, Barney's mum called.
"Did you get Barney to sleep?" she asked.
Nan just grinned.